Aural Time!

Practice Tests for ABRSM and Other Exams

Grade 2

DAVID TURNBULL

CONTENTS

Bosworth

INTRODUCTION

Aural training has always been of the greatest importance to teachers and their pupils. In recent years, however, the emphasis has changed from depending on memory skills to the development of a wider general sense of awareness. The Associated Board of the Royal Schools of Music has given impetus to change by designing new tests for Grade 1 to 5 from January 1993.

Teachers may like to use this booklet to supplement the aural training material they devise for themselves. Like most musical skills, aural awareness needs regular training and practice, and aural work should be part of every lesson.

Not all good instrumental teachers are necessarily fluent pianists. Most of the tests in this booklet therefore have simple pianoforte accompaniments. **If necessary, even these accompaniments can be omitted, and the tests given as melodic lines only.** Much use is made of songs, and it is hoped that the tests will stimulate further interest in this great area of musical achievement.

Teachers may like to use some of the tests in Section A as additional Section D material by using varied dynamics, tempo markings etc.

David Turnbull

September 1992

B. & Co. Ltd., 22287

Test A. Tapping Test.

GRADE 2

Tap the pulse of the piece of music, which will be in 2 (including 6/8) or 3 time. Join in with your tapping as soon as you can, stressing where the strong beats fall. Be prepared to say what time the piece is in.

Tempo di Valse

Waltz from "The Merry Widow" (Franz Lehar)

Moderato

English Nursery Rhyme: *This Old Man*

Lento

English 17th C.: *Drink to me only*

Lento

Welsh trad.: *David of the White Rock*

4

Allegro

English Nursery Rhyme: *Polly Put the Kettle On*

13

mf

Allegretto

English Nursery Rhyme: *Curley Locks*

14

mf

Allegro

English trad.: *The Miller of Dee*

15

mf

Am B

Allegro

English Sea Song: *Riding on a Donkey*

16

mf

Allegro

English Nursery Rhyme: *Here We Go Round the Mulberry Bush*

17

Vif et gai

French Canadian trad.: *L'Alouette* (adapted)

18

Allegro non troppo

Old Provençal Carol

19

Allegro

English Sea Shanty: *Fire Down Below*

20

B. & Co. Ltd., 22287

Test B. Echoes.

Sing, as echoes, three short phrases played to you. The echoes should follow each played phrase in strict time, without an intervening pause. The key-chord and the tonic will first be sounded and the pulse indicated.

Test C. Recognising Changes.

Recognise and explain a rhythmic or melodic change to a two-bar phrase played over twice. The key-chord and tonic will first be sounded.

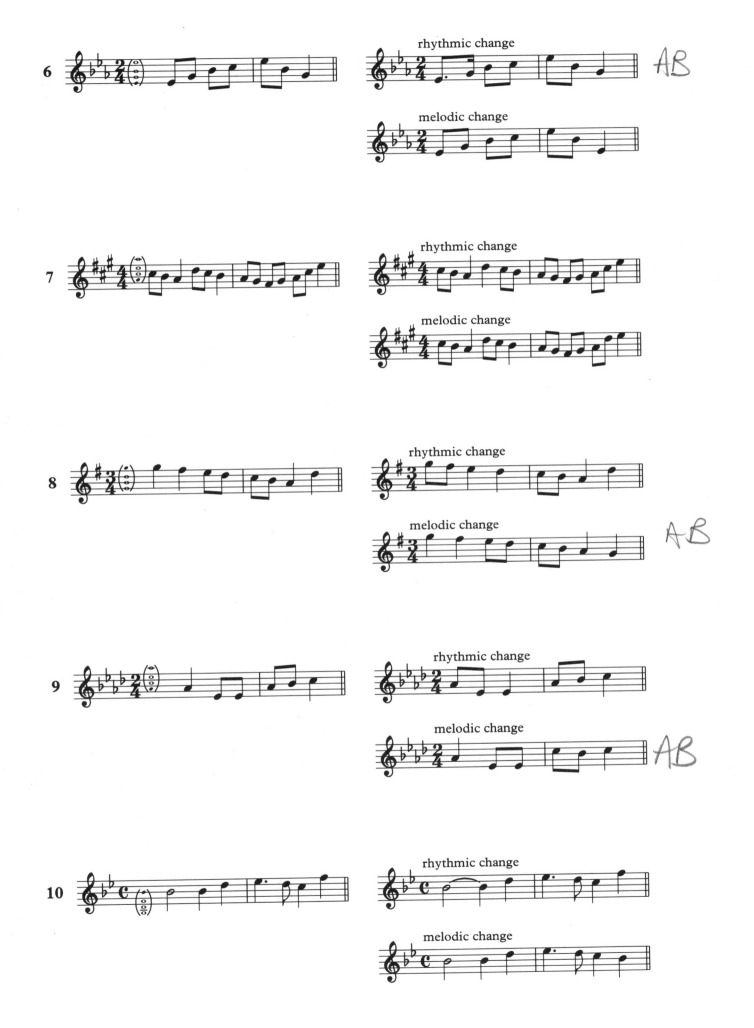

Test D. Recognising Features.

Identify certain features of a piece played over to you. The features will be confined to contrasted dymanics (*p*/*f*), gradation of tone (*crescendo*/*diminuendo*), articulation (*staccato*/*legato*) and recognition of tempo changes (*rallentando*/*accelerando* etc.). Use Italian terms in your answers where appropriate. The piece, or any section of it, can be repeated if neccessary.

Rondeau from "Fairy Queen" (Purcell)

Questions:
 a. Does the music start *piano* or *forte*?
 b. Does it change volume at all? If so, how and where?
 c. Is the music mostly *legato* or *staccato*?
 d. Does the piece stay at the same speed throughout? If not, where does it change, and how?

Rondo (Beethoven)

Questions:
 a. Does the music start *piano* or *forte*?
 b. Does it change volume at all? If so, how and where?
 c. Does the music start *legato* or *staccato*?
 d. Does the piece stay at the same speed throughout? If not, where does it change, and how?

B. & Co. Ltd., 22287

Ecossaise (Beethoven)

Questions:

    a. Does the music start *piano* or *forte*?

    b. Does it change volume at all? If so, how and where?

    c. Is the music mostly *legato* or *staccato*?

    d. Does the piece stay at the same speed throughout? If not, where does it change, and how?

Melody (Schumann) (adapted)

Questions:

    a. Is the music smooth or detached?

    b. Describe the dynamics (*piano/forte, cresc./dim.*).

    c. Are there any changes to the tempo? If so, what happens?

Allegro moderato

From *"Die Fledermaus"* (Johann Strauss II) (adapted)

Questions:

    a. Does the music start *piano* or *forte*?

    b. Does it change volume at all? If so, how and where?

    c. Is the music mostly *legato* or *staccato*, or a mixture of both?

    d. Does the piece stay at the same speed throughout? If not, where does it change, and how?

Allegro non troppo

Le Petit Rien (Couperin)

Questions:

    a. Does the music start *piano* or *forte*?

    b. Does it change volume at all? If so, how and where?

    c. Does the music start *legato* or *staccato*?

    d. Does the piece stay at the same speed throughout? If not, where does it change, and how?

Siciliano (Schumann)

Scherzando

Questions:
a. Is the music at the beginning *legato* or *staccato*?
b. Describe any changes in volume, and say where they occur.
c. Is the tempo held steady throughout? If not, where does it change?

Where the Bee Sucks (Arne)

Allegretto

Questions:
a. Is the music at the beginning *legato* or *staccato*?
b. Does it start *piano* or *forte*?
c. Does it end *piano* or *forte*?
d. Is the tempo held steady throughout? If not, where does it change, and how?

16

From "*Orpheus in the Underworld*" (J. Offenbach)

Allegro

9

Questions:
 a. Does the music start *forte* or *piano*?
 b. Does it change tempo at all? If so, how and where?
 c. Is the music mostly *legato* or *staccato*?

Adagio ma non troppo

Adagio (Steibelt) (adapted)

10

Questions:
 a. Is the music at the beginning *legato* or *staccato*?
 b. Does it start *piano* or *forte*?
 c. Does it end *piano* or *forte*?
 d. Is the tempo held steady throughout? If not, where and how does it change?

Printed and bound in Great Britain by
Caligraving Limited Thetford Norfolk

B. & Co. Ltd., 22287

3/09(169369)